Written by
Bill Abrams

Illustrated by
Carolyn Ewing

The Traditions Of Christmas

TABLE OF CONTENTS

Santa Claus has a very big job to do every Christmas Eve. With no one helping him except his reindeer, he has to deliver presents to all the good little boys and girls on his list in just one night. No wonder he has to spend a whole year resting up before he's ready for next Christmas!

Santa's New Helper

Once there was a little girl named Beth who could not get to sleep on Christmas Eve. She couldn't help thinking about the Christmas tree in the living room, all trimmed with beautiful lights and bows and ornaments. She could hardly wait for Christmas morning to see all the presents under the tree.

But most of all, Beth wanted to stay up and see Santa fill the big stocking her father had helped her pin up on the mantel above the fireplace. She had used one of her mother's long woolen stockings, and she'd put a little sign with her own name on it, so Santa would know it was meant for her gifts.

Her parents tucked her into bed. But soon they heard the door to her room creak open, and there was Beth, asking if Santa had come yet. They

tucked her in again, but sure enough, Beth came out into the living room a few moments later, rubbing her eyes and asking the same question.

After several more times, she was too tired to get out of bed anymore. But she couldn't possibly let her eyes close. Every few minutes she'd call to her parents through the open door and ask when Santa Claus was coming.

At last Beth became too tired to ask the question anymore. She began to dream a wonderful dream. But she wasn't sure it really was a dream, because it seemed so real. It started with the door to her room opening slowly, letting in a little light, and there on the wall was the shadow of a jolly, stout man with a beard and a long hat. The shadow was very familiar.

4

Beth sat up in her bed. Of course she knew who that shadow belonged to. It was Santa Claus! He had come at last. She practically leaped out from under her blankets and raced into the hall. And there he was–dressed all in red, with his shiny black boots and the wide belt, just the way she had always thought of him.

"Ho, ho, ho! Merry Christmas, Beth," he said in his jolly voice. "I understand you've been a good little girl this year and I wonder if you'd like to be my special helper. Would you like that?"

Santa's helper? Would Beth like that job? She'd like that more than anything else she could dream of.

Santa rummaged around inside his big red sack and pulled out a long package wrapped with green paper and a silver bow.

"Do you suppose if I lifted you up and held you just over the mantel, you could drop this gift into the stocking?" asked Santa.

Of course she could!

Beth took the long green package, and as he lifted her high above the mantel, she let the gift fall into the stocking. Part of it stuck out from the top.

"Very good job!" Santa called out heartily. "Ready for another one?"

He found a small red box with a white ribbon. "This one's smaller," he said.

Beth had no trouble dropping the little red box into the stocking, nor the next gift–something flat, wrapped in Christmas tree paper, and still another package–all covered with pretty white doves.

When the stocking was bulging with gifts, and there was no more room for anything else, Santa set her back down on the floor.

"I've got to tell you, you've been a mighty good little helper," he said. "I might even want you back on the job next year. Now you'd better get some rest, little lady. You're going to have a pretty busy day tomorrow. So

goodnight, and merry Christmas."

The next morning, when she woke up, it was Christmas Day! She dashed out of her room to see what Santa had left her, and when she got to the living room, she couldn't believe her eyes.

The first thing she saw was the bulging stocking, just as it had looked in her dream. And there was the same long green package with the silver bow. And when she had gotten the stocking down from the mantel and pulled her gifts out onto the rug, she saw the same small red box she had seen in her dream, and the flat one, and the package all covered with doves.

Only one thing was different. There was a little envelope addressed "To Beth." She opened it up, and she and her mother read it together. It said, "Thank you for being such a good helper, and a wonderful little girl. –Santa Claus."

"Mom," she said, her eyes wide with wonder. "Can a dream be real?"

Her mother and father looked at each other and they both smiled. "Sometimes it can, Beth. Sometimes it can."

A long time ago, people sang and danced to carols all throughout the year, not just at Christmastime. But the best-loved carols were those celebrating the birth of Jesus, and they are the ones that are still sung today, by people all over the world.

Let Heaven And Nature Sing

Three singers were rehearsing a carol in an old church, for Christmas Eve service. They had sung together many times before. But tonight they were trying to create the most beautiful version of "Joy to the World" anyone had ever heard. They wanted to give the congregation music that would linger in their ears and in their memories long after the holiday. But for some reason, the rehearsal was not going well.

"Must be the weather," joked the first singer.

"Could be we're tired," said the second singer.

"Maybe we need an audience," smiled the third.

They started the carol yet again. They had only sung for a few seconds when the third singer stopped and said, "I heard something. Like an echo."

The others told him it was just his imagination. But when they began to sing once more, there it was–that same echo. They could all hear it now, every time there was a pause. It was coming from the balcony of the church.

"What do you suppose?" asked the first singer.

"Never heard it before," said the second.

"Let's take a look," said the third singer.

One by one, they climbed the long, narrow stairs that led to the darkened balcony. When they reached the top they discovered a small boy trying to hide behind a pew.

"Was it you making that noise?" asked the first singer.

"What are you doing here in the dark?" asked the third singer.

The frightened boy couldn't get a word out. He just stood there, his eyes wide open.

The second singer scratched her head, not quite sure what to make of him. "Well," she said, finally. "If you want to stay up here and just listen, it's okay. But not a peep out of you."

The boy nodded his agreement, and the three singers trudged back downstairs and took their places once more.

But no sooner had they begun to sing than they heard the echo again, coming from the same place. The third singer rushed up to the balcony, taking the stairs two at a time. There was the scared little boy again. The singer was just about to say something to him when a gleam came into his eyes. Without a word, he turned and went back down the stairs to join the others.

"I think I've got a pretty good idea about that echo," said the third singer, chuckling. "Let's just see if I'm right."

Yet again, they started to sing the carol, wanting to make it special. But before they were halfway through, the third singer stopped. He had heard the echo once again.

He motioned to the others to keep singing the carol. Then, quiet as a cat, he crept up the narrow staircase to the balcony. As he entered the darkness for the third time, a sudden smile lit up his face. He was right about the "echo" after all.

There was the boy, standing in a thin beam of moonlight that came through the stained glass window. He was singing the carol along with the others. It was "Joy to the World" the way the older singer had never heard it before, with a soaring beauty that brought joy to his ears and to his heart.

He listened for a moment, and then as the boy continued to sing, the third singer tiptoed back downstairs as fast as he could. Motioning to the others to keep on singing and to follow him, the third singer led the way back up to the balcony.

The boy's singing was now even more beautiful than he had heard it a moment ago. It was clear and pure, and it filled the church with the sound he knew would make this Christmas Eve service the most memorable ever.

As the last note of the carol lingered in the far corners of the church, the second singer turned on the lights, revealing the tall ceiling, the pews, and the boy, shy and fearful.

The three singers smiled at him to take away his fear.

"You've got some voice," said the first singer, gazing at the boy in wonder.

"A voice like yours doesn't belong in the dark," said the second.

"Everyone should hear it," said the third.

The three singers exchanged glances. Each one knew exactly what was in the others' minds, and the third singer said it for all of them.

11

"Son, what are you doing Christmas Eve?" he asked.

"How'd you like to sing with us?" the second singer asked.

"Oh, yes," said the boy. "Oh, yes." They were the first words the three singers had heard him say. And he could not stop saying "Yes, yes, yes," as he ran home to ask his parents.

It was the most beautiful Christmas Eve service the congregation could remember. And the highlight was the boy and the three older singers, caroling "Joy to the World" as it had never been sung before.

Many would never again sit under the tall ceiling without hearing the high, soaring sound of the boy's voice singing the carol. It would live in their memories and in their hearts forever.

One of the most exciting holidays of the year for Hispanic families is Three Kings Day, celebrated January 6th for the Kings who came to Bethlehem riding on camels, bearing gifts for Jesus. As time went by, children began to leave out straw and water for the camels. In gratitude, the Kings began to leave gifts for the children.

Grandpa's Surprise

The three Perez children were sorry that Christmas was over, with all its excitement and gifts. New Year's Day had come and gone. And now all they had to look forward to was the bitter cold and biting winds of winter in Chicago.

"Aren't you forgetting something?" asked Grandpa, smiling his sunniest smile. He had come up from Puerto Rico to be with the family for the holiday season.

Laura couldn't think of anything they had forgotten. Neither could Steven or Michael, the youngest Perez child (the one Grandpa liked to call "Miguel").

"Why, in just three days it's going to be Three Kings Day," said Grandpa.

"What's that?" asked Michael.

"You mean your mother and father didn't tell you about Three Kings Day?" asked Grandpa, raising his shaggy eyebrows. "That's one of the best days of the year in Puerto Rico. The whole family gets together. We play music and sing carols. Then there's a special dinner and we give each other presents."

"Don't they give presents on Christmas Day in Puerto Rico?" asked Laura.

"Of course they do," replied Grandpa. "But don't you remember the story of the Three Kings who brought presents from the Orient when Jesus was born?"

"Kaspar, Melchior and Balthasar," Steven recalled proudly.

"Hey, very good!" said Grandpa. "They rode all the way on their camels, following a star to Bethlehem. And do you know what gifts they brought?"

Laura quickly answered, "Gold, Frankincense and Myrrh!"

"Good for you," said Grandpa. "Now can you imagine how tired the camels must have been coming all that way?"

"Oh, very tired," said Michael.

Grandpa continued, "Well, if you leave out a little bit of straw and some water for the camels, the Kings would be very grateful. Sometimes, they even leave a gift behind."

That settled it. Grandpa promised the children they would celebrate Three Kings Day, but on one condition: that they make the holiday a surprise for their parents.

The children readily agreed. "They gave us so many surprises at Christmas," said Laura. "And they worked so hard. It would be wonderful to give Mom and Dad a big surprise now."

The night before, Grandpa and the children spent hours getting ready. First they found some clothes in Mom's closet, then they borrowed some towels from the bathroom.

While the other children were helping Mom with the dinner dishes, Michael and Grandpa found a big cup and a box. They filled the cup with water and the box with leaves that had fallen off the big plant near the front window. Then they placed them in Mom and Dad's bedroom.

"Miguel, you're supposed to put out water and real straw for the Three Kings' camels," explained Grandpa. "But these leaves are the best we've got. And I'm sure they won't mind."

"It's just like putting out a snack for Santa and his reindeer!" said Michael.

Mom and Dad didn't find the cup and the box until the next morning, when they woke up. "Hey, what's this doing here?" Mom called out.

"You don't know?" Grandpa called back.

Not a moment later, Grandpa's old guitar was heard playing a familiar

melody, but one Mom just couldn't place. And then she heard the words, sung to the guitar by her children:

"Los Tres Santos Reyes"
"Los tres y los tres."

"Of course!" she said, turning to her husband with a big, broad smile as she recognized the traditional carol. "'Los Tres Santos Reyes'–the Three Kings. How could I forget Three Kings Day?"

The door to their bedroom burst open, and the singing children, with towels wrapped around their heads like turbans, wearing long robes from their mother's closet, came in.

"We are the Three Kings," they said when the song was over, "and you must follow us with your eyes closed."

Taking their parents' hands they led them out of the bedroom and into the dining room, making sure their parents' eyes were closed all the time.

"You may open them, now!" said Grandpa.

"The gift of The First King to the best mother in the world," said Laura in her deepest voice, placing a platter of steaming eggs and sausage on the table.

"The gift of The Second King to the best father in the world," said Steven, setting down a plateful of toast and jam.

"The gift of The Third King to the best parents," said Michael, putting a bowl of fruit on the table.

"What a delicious-looking breakfast!" said Mom.

"And look what the Three Kings brought for you," Grandpa said to the children, pointing at three small packages under the table.

"I think we've just established a new tradition in this family," Dad smiled.

"A very old tradition," said Grandpa.

"A very good old tradition," agreed Mom, beaming at Grandpa and her three little kings.

In southern Italy, the Christmas feast is shared with friends and relatives and takes place on Christmas Eve instead of Christmas Day. Chicken or turkey might be on the table, but the main course is usually fish, prepared with a special sauce, and accompanied by panettone (currant bread), artichokes cooked with eggs, and cannoli, a creamy pastry dessert.

A Feast To Remember

The talk and the laughter and the singing rang throughout the house. It was the traditional Christmas Eve feast at the Bono Vineyard. As usual, Vincent Bono had gathered his children, grandchildren, other relatives and old friends in the large California farmhouse nestled in the Sonoma Valley.

Marie Bono had been cooking for days. This morning she had awakened early to bake loaves of currant bread, whose rich aroma found its way to every corner of the house. She had stuffed three large chickens with rice and mushrooms and small onions, and set them into the oven to roast. And for the final touch, she covered her famous baked salmon with her delicate lemon sauce.

Then to the delight of everyone, Marie proudly brought out each

21

course, one after the other. There was wine from the finest grapes of the vineyard. Everyone around the table was bursting with satisfaction and holiday cheer.

Vincent beamed with pleasure, thankful for today's celebration and for all that life had brought him. After a moment, his smile came to rest on Joey, his oldest grandchild, who had spent many Saturday afternoons fishing with his grandfather.

"I'll tell you something I've never told anyone before," Vincent said. "The first year we came to the valley, did you know we came this close to moving away?" He made his forefinger almost touch his thumb.

"You never told us that, Grandpa," Joey said.

"It was on the day before Christmas. We were just starting out, and it wasn't easy. We had practically no money, and there were only the two of us to plant the new vines, fix up the farmhouse, keep the second-hand equipment running, and get ready for the birth of our first baby. By the way, that baby was your father."

"Really Grandpa?"

By now, everyone at the table was listening to Vincent's story. He caught his wife's eye at the other end of the table.

"Your grandmother never lost faith in the future," Vincent continued. "Though I almost did, just before Christmas Eve. We had no money for gifts, so we decided our present to each other would be a wonderful Christmas dinner. But we were having a lot of problems with our car, and with one thing and another, we had put off shopping for food until the last minute.

"We set out for town, finally. But can you imagine what happened halfway down the driveway?" He saw a knowing smile on Joey's face.

"You guessed it. Our poor, old, tired car died on us, once and for all. And what seemed even worse at that moment, there was no way of getting into town to buy Christmas dinner. It was the last straw.

"I'm ashamed to say it, Joey, but I threw my hands into the air and roared. And then I kicked the car again and again, as if it were to blame for our bad luck. And when I had gotten out my anger, I just sat down on one of the fenders and stared into the distance."

"You almost gave up," his wife said quietly.

"Vincent? Give up?" someone said at the other end of the table.

"Not you, Grandpa," said Joey.

"It's true. I think I'd still be sitting there, staring at nothing, if it hadn't been for what your Grandma did just then. She took my hand and led me back into the house, telling me to leave the car where it was, because we were going to have our Christmas dinner after all.

"I wondered what in the world she was talking about. As far as I knew, there was hardly a bit of food in the house. Little did I know what she had in store for us!

"She asked me to reach up to the top cabinet in the kitchen and see what I could find there. It was too high to see anything, but I felt four cans and a small cube, and I brought them down. They were canned beans, corn, tomatoes and carrots, and a cube of beef bouillon. This was going to be Christmas dinner? I couldn't believe it.

" 'You think those are just four cans and a cube of bouillon?' she asked.

" 'That's what they look like to me,' I said.

" 'You are actually looking at the most magnificent, most wonderful minestrone soup anyone ever made. Just the thing to begin a Christmas feast,' she said.

"Aha! I was beginning to understand. Your grandmother asked me to check the lower kitchen cabinet. I discovered a box of spaghetti and took it out.

"'I suppose you're going to tell me this isn't just a box of spaghetti, but your special holiday pasta dish, fit for the finest table,' I said, with a twinkle in my eye.

"'No restaurant ever served better,' she replied, taking out the eggs, milk, butter and Parmesan cheese which were just about the only things left in the refrigerator and placing them in front of me. 'Of course it needs a great sauce. Would you care to do the honors?'

"'But of course, Signora,' I said, bowing to her. 'If the chef wouldn't mind preparing the minestrone soup.'

"'It's quite difficult to make,' she said, starting to open one of the cans, 'But I'll certainly do my best.'

"There was one can left in the cabinet. It was apple sauce. 'May I suggest hot apple sauce with cinnamon as the perfect dessert to finish our

Christmas feast?' I said.

"'It will be even better than your mother's cannoli,' she said.

"When the dinner was ready, we set out the silver candlesticks we had gotten as a wedding present on our one good linen tablecloth. And never did our table look more beautiful than that Christmas Eve. The minestrone soup, the spaghetti and the spicy apple sauce made the loveliest Christmas feast I can remember. And I wouldn't have traded it for anything.

"Later that evening, we lit a fire and sang Christmas carols until long after midnight."

"It sounds like you had a very good time that night, Grandpa," said Joey.

"Oh, we were very happy that Christmas Eve," his grandmother agreed, blushing.

"And very thankful we had each other," Vincent said, looking at his wife. "I realized that night, that's all we really needed, even if we didn't have much else."

"Sometimes the feast is in the heart," said Marie.

"I think that meal was the best Christmas gift we ever gave each other," Vincent said.

"And if it kept you from moving away, it was a gift to everyone here," said one of the guests, raising his glass. "To La Famiglia Bono."

"La Famiglia Bono," everyone said.

Long ago in Germany, to celebrate Christmas, families made wooden pyramids with steps or shelves, and placed small candles on them. These became known as "Christmas Pyramids," and were later decorated with evergreen twigs, glass balls, tinsel, and the Star of Bethlehem. The modern Christmas tree developed from this tradition hundreds of years later.

The Tree Of Life

We lived in the country, on the edge of a deep forest, and from the moment our son Daniel could talk, he loved trees. He loved to climb them, to play beneath their branches and just to be with them. He could sit for hours listening to the wind rustle through their leaves. Daniel gave names to the trees he liked, the way other children name animals. "Simon," "Sampson" and "Max" were some of the names I remember.

There was something magical about it. Every day he used to say good morning to his trees. And when the branches blew in the wind, you could almost imagine the trees were saying good morning to him.

His favorite tree, a blue spruce, must have been well over a hundred years old. It was the one he called "Simon." It towered over us as we stood beneath its branches, which were so dense that hardly a ray of sun found its way to the floor of the quiet clearing where it grew, deep in a neighbor's woods.

The story about "Simon" happened the year we decided to spend Christmas visiting Daniel's uncle, who lived in New York City. It was a marvelous city during the Christmas season, with brightly lit stores and holiday shoppers bustling along the avenues.

Daniel was getting excited about our visit. He asked me if there were any trees in New York, and I told him they grew out of the sidewalks, and that there was a whole bunch in Central Park.

One morning, just as the time for our trip drew near, we had our first snowfall. Daniel and I set out for a walk in the forest. It was so quiet and still, with the fresh snow covering the branches. It was a special moment for us.

A week later we were awakened by the high-pitched scream of a chain saw coming from the woods. Daniel was the first to spring out of bed, followed by the rest of the family. Even from far away, the sound shattered the peace and quiet of the morning.

Quickly we got dressed and raced into the woods, as fast as we could run. But we were too late. We heard the rumble of a huge timber truck fading into the distance as we reached the clearing. All that was left of the great blue spruce was a stump, its raw surface glistening with sap.

I had never seen Daniel look the way he looked just then. He didn't move. He didn't speak. Not a word, not even a tear. I picked him up and gently carried him home.

The next day, Daniel said very little. He wouldn't smile. He hardly touched his meals.

Daniel started to feel more like himself a few days later—except for two things. He would never talk about "Simon" and he still wouldn't smile. Not even the anticipation of our visit to New York could make his face light up.

In the car, on the way to New York City, his mother and I tried to cheer him up with our favorite carols, but Daniel just stared out the window. Promises of toy stores and a holiday meal with his cousins the next day didn't help.

We reached the hotel just as the sun was going down. It had been a long drive, and my wife suggested we all needed a walk before dinner. We headed for Fifth Avenue, where all the large department stores were still lit up for the holidays and crowded with last-minute shoppers.

As we walked around, we found it hard to get into the Christmas spirit despite the cheerful people swirling around us, and the bright sound of trumpets playing "God Rest You Merry, Gentlemen." Daniel's sadness had set us apart.

We crossed the street to walk back to the hotel, when I had an idea. I thought perhaps the sight of the skaters at Rockefeller Plaza would make us all a bit merrier. My wife and Daniel agreed reluctantly.

And that's when it happened. As we reached the Plaza where the elegant white angels pointed the way to the skating rink, I stole a glance at Daniel. He was staring at something in the distance, and as I watched, I saw a smile begin at the corners of his mouth. Then it grew and grew until his whole face was glowing.

Puzzled, I followed his eyes to the end of the mall. And then I saw it, too. Towering above the skating rink, radiant with light, was the unmistakable shape of a huge blue spruce.

I don't know how, but Daniel knew instantly that it was his blue spruce, "Simon."

Daniel's "Simon" had been selected as the great Christmas tree for all New York!

We stood and watched the crowds of people gazing in wonder at the beauty of the tree, just as we had done when it was in the forest.

A sense of joy suddenly came over me. The tree was a wonderful gift—not just for our family as it had been in the forest, but for everyone, bringing all who saw it joy and gladness for Christmas.

I reached for Daniel's hand. Never had I seen such a radiant face. And I knew he felt just what I was feeling at that moment.

"Dad!" he said. "Now everybody can be 'Simon's' friend."

In all our days, I will never experience a more special Christmas than that one. And I doubt that Daniel will either.

Art Direction by Jean Pierre Langlois